Flute Exam Pack

ABRSM Grade 2

Selected from the 2018–2021 syllabus

Name

Date of exam

Contents

page

LIST A

1 **Jacques Offenbach** Can-Can: from *Orphée aux enfers*, Act II, arr. David Blackwell   2

2 **Johann Christian Schickhardt** Vivace: Seventh movement from Sonata in D, Op. 30 No. 11   3

3 **Trad. English** O Soldier, Soldier, arr. Alan Bullard   4

LIST B

1 **Alan Jay Lerner & Frederick Loewe** Wouldn't It Be Loverly?: from *My Fair Lady*, arr. Nancy Litten   5

2 **Christopher Norton** A Walk by the Sea: from *The Microjazz Flute Collection 1*   6

3 **Sergey Prokofiev** Troika: No. 4 from *Lieutenant Kijé* Suite, Op. 60, arr. David Blackwell   7

LIST C

1 **Helen Madden** Silver Riddle: No. 6 from *20 Fantastic Flute Studies*   8

2 **Richard Michael** The Jazz Waltz Blues   9

3 **Trad. Scottish** Loch Lomond, arr. ABRSM   10

Scales and arpeggios   12

Sight-reading   14

Consultant Editor for ABRSM: David Blackwell
Footnotes: Anthony Burton and Richard Jones (RJ)

Other pieces for Grade 2

LIST A

4 **J. Clarke** Trumpet Tune, arr. Wagner. *Classical Music for Children for Flute* (Schott)

5 **Handel** Bourrée (from *Music for the Royal Fireworks*, HWV 351), arr. Lawrance. *Winner Scores All for Flute* (Brass Wind)

6 **Hook** He Piped So Sweet, arr. Emerson. *An English Garland, Vol. 1* (Emerson)

7 **Mozart** Papageno's Bell Tune (from *The Magic Flute*), arr. McDowall. *Harlequin, Book 1* (Cramer)

8 **Tchaikovsky** Ancient French Song, arr. McDowall. *Harlequin, Book 1* (Cramer)

9 **Petzold** Menuet in G, arr. Denley. *Time Pieces for Flute, Vol. 1* (ABRSM)

10 **Vivaldi** Winter (from *The Four Seasons*), arr. Lawrance. *Winners Galore for Flute* (Brass Wind)

LIST B

4 **Andersson & Ulvaeus** I have a dream, arr. Hammond. *Ten Top Pops for Flute* (Kevin Mayhew)

5 **Phil Coulter & Bill Martin** Puppet on a String, arr. Lawrance. *Winners Galore for Flute* (Brass Wind)

6 **Humperdinck** Brother, come and dance with me (from *Hänsel und Gretel*), arr. Denley. *Time Pieces for Flute, Vol. 1* (ABRSM)

7 **Mick Jagger & Keith Richards** Paint it Black, arr. Hart. *Hartbeat* (Brass Wind)

8 **Duncan Lamont** Mr Benn: from *Mr Benn for Flute* (Queen's Temple Publications)

9 **Andrew Lloyd Webber** Starlight Express, arr. Lawrance. *Winner Scores All for Flute* (Brass Wind)

10 **Cecilia McDowall** Circus Rag. *Harlequin, Book 1* (Cramer)

LIST C

4 **Anon.** Hessian Dance, arr. Harris & Adams. No. 19 from *76 Graded Studies for Flute, Book 1* (Faber)

5 **Alan Bullard** Nimble Flute *or* Dancing Flute: No. 8 *or* No. 10 from *Fifty for Flute, Book 1* (ABRSM)

6 **E. Köhler** Study in A minor. No. 24 from *125 Easy Classical Studies for Flute* (Universal)

7 **Mark Nightingale** New Document: No. 4 from *Jazz@Etudes for Flute* (Warwick Music)

8 **James Rae** Little March of the Soldier Ants: No. 4 from *42 More Modern Studies for Solo Flute* (Universal)

9 **Philip Sparke** Square Dance *or* Melody in C: No. 16 *or* No. 17 from *Skilful Studies for Flute* (Anglo Music)

10 **Trad. Chinese** Jasmine Flower, arr. Adams & Harris. No. 13 from *More Graded Studies for Flute, Book 1* (Faber)

First published in 2017 by ABRSM (Publishing) Ltd,
a wholly owned subsidiary of ABRSM, 4 London Wall Place,
London EC2Y 5AU, United Kingdom
© 2017 by The Associated Board of the Royal Schools of Music
Distributed worldwide by Oxford University Press

Music origination by Julia Bovee and Katie Johnston (Sight-reading)
Cover by Kate Benjamin & Andy Potts
Printed in England by Caligraving Ltd, Thetford, Norfolk
on materials from sustainable sources.
P14526

Can-Can

from *Orphée aux enfers*, Act II

Arranged by David Blackwell

Jacques Offenbach
(1819–80)

The can-can is a lively dance, popular in mid-19th-century Paris, performed by a line of high-kicking women. The best-known example is riotously danced and sung in Offenbach's 1858 comic opera *Orpheus in the Underworld*, a farcical retelling of the classical legend of Orpheus and Eurydice. **The repeat should be observed in the exam.**

Vivace

Seventh movement from Sonata in D, Op. 30 No. 11

Edited by and continuo
realization by Richard Jones

J. C. Schickhardt
(c.1682–1762)

This Vivace has the character of a fast and lively minuet. It is the finale of Schickhardt's Sonata No. 11 in D from his *L'Alphabet de la musique*, Op. 30, a set of 24 sonatas in all the keys for flute (or recorder or violin) and continuo. Johann Christian Schickhardt was a German woodwind player who settled in Leiden, Holland. (RJ)

Source: *L'Alphabet de la Musique, contenant XXIV Sonates=Solos pour la Flûte traversière*, Op. 30 (London, c. 1735). All dynamics are editorial suggestions only, as are the slurs in b. 18 and the trill in b. 20.

© 1995 by The Associated Board of the Royal Schools of Music
Adapted from *Baroque Flute Pieces*, Book I, edited by Richard Jones (ABRSM)

O Soldier, Soldier

Arranged by Alan Bullard

Trad. English

O Soldier, Soldier is a well-known English folk song in which a girl repeatedly asks 'O soldier, soldier, won't you marry me?' The soldier replies each time 'Oh no, sweet maid, I cannot marry thee', citing as the reason an article of clothing that he lacks for the ceremony – but the girl finds him everything he needs. Finally he comes up with a better reason for a refusal: 'for I have a wife of my own!' The firm rhythm of a military march and the marked articulation bring out the humour of the song.

Wouldn't It Be Loverly?

from *My Fair Lady*

Arranged by Nancy Litten

A. J. Lerner (1918–86) and
Frederick Loewe (1901–88)

B:1

My Fair Lady was a smash hit musical in New York in 1956 and later in London and on film, written by the well-known partnership of Lerner (words) and Loewe (music), and based on George Bernard Shaw's play *Pygmalion*. In early 20th-century London, Eliza Doolittle, a poor flower seller, is taken into the household of a professor of phonetics, taught to speak good English and passed off as a member of polite society. Early in the show, Eliza and her friends imagine what it would be like to lead a comfortable life. Their song has the recurring refrain (as in bars 9–10) 'Wouldn't it be loverly', the last word being the Cockney (London dialect) pronunciation of 'lovely'.

B:2

A Walk by the Sea

from *The Microjazz Flute Collection 1*

Christopher Norton
(born 1953)

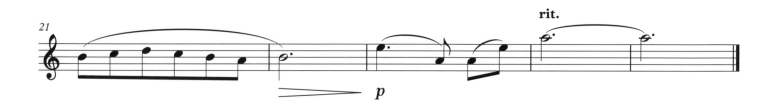

Christopher Norton moved in 1977 from New Zealand to Britain, where he quickly established a reputation as a composer of educational music in popular styles, notably the successful *Microjazz* series. His *A Walk by the Sea* has a piano accompaniment suggesting the gentle rise and fall of the waves, and a flute part expressing a mood of contentment.

Troika

No. 4 from *Lieutenant Kijé* Suite, Op. 60

B:3

Arranged by David Blackwell

Sergey Prokofiev
(1891–1953)

Lieutenant Kijé is a film made in Russia in 1933, a satire on official bureaucracy: its title character is a soldier accidentally created in the records by a slip of a clerk's pen, and then kept 'alive', on paper at least, through an eventful career. Prokofiev's music for the film has become popular in the concert hall in the form of a five-movement 'symphonic suite'. A 'troika' is a three-horse sleigh, and the music of this movement – now a favourite at Christmas time – accompanies a journey across the snow when Kijé is sent into exile in Siberia.

Silver Riddle

No. 6 from *20 Fantastic Flute Studies*

Helen Madden
(born 1974)

Helen Madden is musical director of a school of music in Yorkshire, in the north of England, and an experienced teacher, performer, improviser and composer. She advises players to give this piece 'a mysterious and spooky feel'.

The Jazz Waltz Blues

Richard Michael
(born 1949)

Richard Michael is a leading jazz composer, performer (on keyboards), educator and broadcaster in Scotland, and has been associated for many years with the Fife Youth Jazz Orchestra. In his *Jazz Waltz Blues*, the phrasing – for example, the slurs across the beat in bars 13 and 15 – adds to the music's carefree character.

C:3

Loch Lomond

Arranged by ABRSM

Trad. Scottish

Loch Lomond is a well-known traditional Scottish song, originally a lament following the defeat of the Jacobite rebels by the English army in 1745. The final phrase includes, in bar 15, two examples of the short–long rhythmic figure known as the 'Scotch snap'.

Scales and arpeggios

SCALES

from memory
tongued *and* slurred

one octave   ♩ = 56

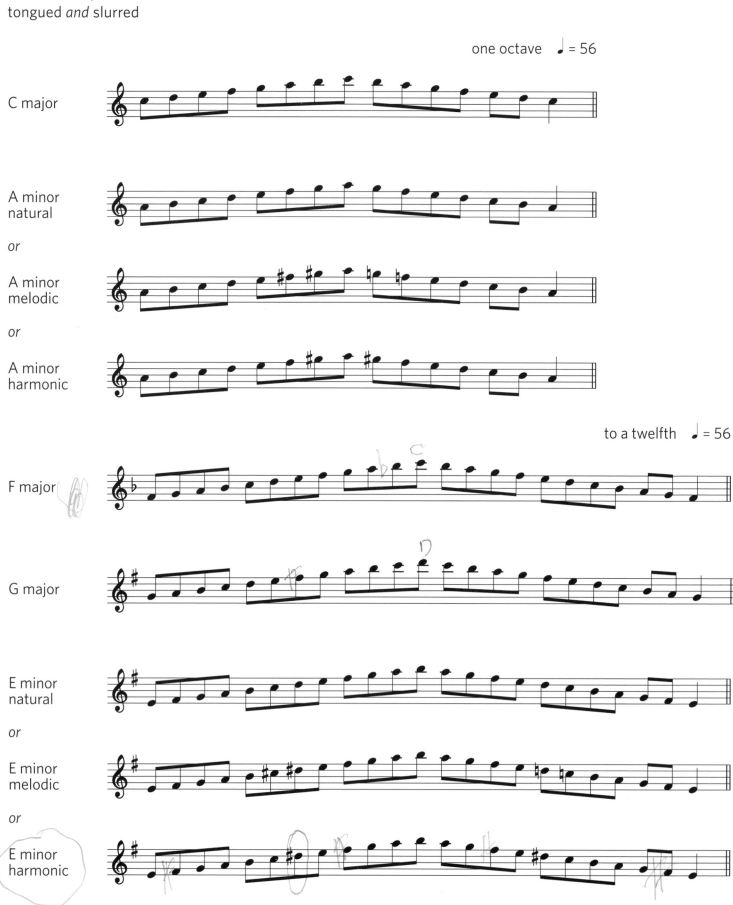

to a twelfth   ♩ = 56

ARPEGGIOS

from memory
tongued *and* slurred

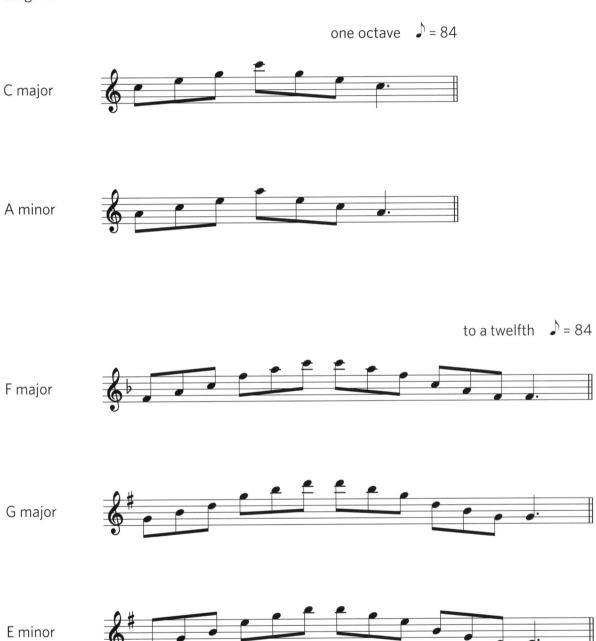

Sight-reading

Sight-reading

Sight-reading